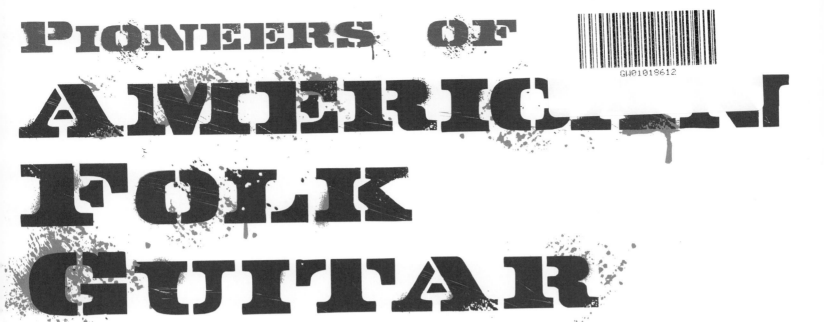

PIONEERS OF AMERICAN FOLK GUITAR

WISE PUBLICATIONS
part of The Music Sales Group
London / New York / Paris / Sydney / Copenhagen / Berlin / Madrid /Hong Kong/ Tokyo

Published by
Wise Publications
14-15 Berners Street,
London W1T 3LJ, UK.

Exclusive Distributors:
Music Sales Limited
Distribution Centre, Newmarket Road,
Bury St Edmunds, Suffolk IP33 3YB, UK.
Music Sales Corporation
180 Madison Avenue, 24th Floor,
New York NY 10010, USA.
Music Sales Pty Limited
Units 3-4, 17 Willfox Street, Condell Park
NSW 2200, Australia.

Order No. AM1005598
ISBN 978-1-78038-758-1

This book © Copyright 2012 Wise Publications,
a division of Music Sales Limited.

Edited by Adrian Hopkins.
Cover design by Ruth Keating.
Music arranged by Matt Cowe.
Music processed by Paul Ewers Music Design.

Photos courtesy of:
Artist: John Fahey (Photo by Michael Ochs Archives/Getty Images)
          Chet Atkins (Photo by Michael Ochs Archives/Corbis)
          Paul Simon (Photo by RB/Redferns)
          Elizabeth Cotten (Photo by John Cohen/Getty Images)
          Mississippi John Hurt (Photo by Michael Ochs Archives/Getty Images)
          Bob Dylan (Photo by Val Wilmer/Redferns)
          Dave Van Ronk (Photo by David Redfern/Redferns)
          Jorma Kaukonen (Photo by Tim Mosenfelder/Getty Images)
          Leo Kottke (Photo by Michael Ochs Archives/Getty Images)

With special thanks to Michael Gulezian and John Stropes.

Printed in the EU.

Your Guarantee of Quality
As publishers, we strive to produce every book to the
highest commercial standards.
This book has been carefully designed to minimise awkward
page turns and to make playing from it a real pleasure.
Particular care has been given to specifying acid-free, neutral-sized paper
made from pulps which have not been elemental chlorine bleached.
This pulp is from farmed sustainable forests and was
produced with special regard for the environment.
Throughout, the printing and binding have been planned to
ensure a sturdy, attractive publication which should give years of enjoyment.
If your copy fails to meet our high standards,
please inform us and we will gladly replace it.

www.musicsales.com

CONTENTS

CANDY MAN BLUES
MISSISSIPPI JOHN HURT
32

EMBRYONIC JOURNEY
JORMA KAUKONEN
12

FREIGHT TRAIN
ELIZABETH COTTEN
16

GIRL FROM THE NORTH COUNTRY
BOB DYLAN
20

A HAZY SHADE OF WINTER
SIMON & GARFUNKEL
26

IAN AND NISA
MICHAEL GULEZIAN
37

ICE MINER
LEO KOTTKE
42

ON THE SUNNY SIDE OF THE OCEAN
JOHN FAHEY
50

THE POOR PEOPLE OF PARIS
CHET ATKINS
56

REDWOOD RAMBLE
ROBBIE BASHO
60

ST. LOUIS TICKLE
DAVE VAN RONK
45

TURNPIKE TERROR
PETER LANG
68

CANDY MAN BLUES

MISSISSIPPI JOHN HURT

Original release: *Stack O' Lee/Candy Man Blues*
78 rpm single (1928)

Compared to his more flamboyant contemporaries, Mississippi John Hurt was an unassuming, softly-spoken man, yet he was a highly influential player, whose music contributed to the development of modern blues, country, bluegrass and folk. His 'Candy Man Blues' became a favourite song for those who found his music in the sixties following its rediscovery by folk musicologist Tom Hoskins.

EMBRYONIC JOURNEY

JORMA KAUKONEN

Original release: *Surrealistic Pillow* (1967)

Although perhaps best known for his work with Jefferson Airplane and Hot Tuna, Jorma Kaukonen's accomplished solo work has seen him become an icon for many folk guitarists. Although released by Jefferson Airplane, 'Embryonic Journey' is purely a solo affair. This song reached a new audience of over 50 million when it featured in the final episode of the long-running American sitcom *Friends* in 2004.

FREIGHT TRAIN

ELIZABETH COTTEN

Original release: *Volume 3: When I'm Gone* (1979)

A self-taught left-handed guitarist, Elizabeth Cotten developed her own distinct style which became known as 'Cotten picking'; playing the bass lines with her fingers and the melody with her thumb. She played a right-handed guitar, strung for right-handed playing and usually in standard tuning, essentially playing the instrument upside down. With money earned through working as a domestic helper, Cotten bought her first guitar and was writing her own songs by her early teens, one of which was 'Freight Train'. Written about the trains that would pass by her house on Lloyd Street in Carrboro, North Carolina, the song would go on to be one of her most recognised.

GIRL FROM THE NORTH COUNTRY

BOB DYLAN

Original release: *The Freewheelin' Bob Dylan* (1963)

From Delta blues through to gospel, country and rock, Bob Dylan has explored an array of styles and genres throughout his prolific career. However, his folk period of the early sixties is his most celebrated and iconic, with songs such as 'Blowin' In The Wind', 'The Times Are A-Changin'' and 'A Hard Rain's a-Gonna Fall' now established in American pop culture. Written following Dylan's first trip to England in December 1962, 'Girl From The North Country' was influenced by his exposure to the repertoire of traditional English ballads through folksinger Martin Carthy, whose own arrangement of 'Scarborough Fair' is thought to have inspired the song's melody line and lyrics. Try and maintain a steady thumb rhythm throughout.

A HAZY SHADE OF WINTER

SIMON & GARFUNKEL

Original release: *A Hazy Shade of Winter/
For Emily, Whenever I May Find Her* Single (1966)

Although performed by both Simon and Garfunkel,
'A Hazy Shade of Winter' was written by Paul Simon, with his 12-string guitar a
prominent feature of the song's composition. The song, which covers the passage of
seasons, specifically the gloom of winter, was the duo's second biggest hit after
'Mrs. Robinson'. The combination of the capo at the fifth fret and the doubled
strings both help create a bright tone and some distinctive harmonic ideas,
especially on the G chord of the chorus. Try and pay particular attention to
Simon's right hand, as he doesn't tend to stick to one picking pattern throughout.

IAN AND NISA

MICHAEL GULEZIAN

Original release: *Unspoken Intentions*
(1980)

Michael Gulezian began playing guitar at
the age of six. He has become one of the most
highly-regarded solo acoustic guitarists on
the American scene, offering masterclasses
and guitar workshops outside of his busy
touring schedule. John Fahey spoke highly of
Gulezian's debut album, saying: "...this record while taking up within itself all
previous American acoustic guitar styles..., goes further and far beyond anything
that has hitherto been accomplished."

ICE MINER

LEO KOTTKE

Original release: *Mudlark* (1971)

Celebrated for his distinctive fingering technique,
Leo Kottke rose to prominence despite suffering
damage to the hearing in both ears during
his youth. After hitching across the USA, he settled
in Minneapolis, becoming a regular on the local
folk scene. His major breakthrough came when Kottke's
second album, *Circle Round the Sun* came to the attention of
John Fahey and his manager who encouraged Capitol to sign the guitarist.

ON THE SUNNY SIDE OF THE OCEAN

JOHN FAHEY

Original release: *The Transfiguration
of Blind Joe Death* (1965)

With its abstract, implied melody and intricate picking pattern,
'On The Sunny Side Of The Ocean' is a favourite amongst Fahey's
many admirers. Composed in an open G major tuning (D-G-D-G-B-D),
it's a bold piece of bluesy inflections and well-worked
dissonance. The title is a play on Hank Snow's 'The Sunny Side
of the Mountain' and it was originally released in 1965 on Fahey's
fourth album, *The Transfiguration of Blind Joe Death*, originally
in a hand-lettered edition of 50. This version appeared on the compilation *Leo Kottke,
Peter Lang, John Fahey*, released by Takoma records in 1974.

THE POOR PEOPLE OF PARIS

CHET ATKINS

Original release: *The Poor People of Paris/Honey* Single (1955)

Credited with developing the Nashville sound along with Owen Bradley, the virtuoso finger picking style of Chet Atkins won him admirers across the American music spectrum as he explored and played with folk and country sounds. If you're finding it too difficult, try playing just the bass line to begin with.

REDWOOD RAMBLE

ROBBIE BASHO

Original release: *Bonn Ist Supreme* (2008)

Although recorded in 1980, Robbie Basho's *Bonn Ist Supreme* didn't see the light of day through an official release until 2008. Throughout his 20-year career, Basho sought to expand the vocabulary and reach of the steel string acoustic guitar by combining many different influences together. Like 'Girl From the North Country', concentrate on maintaining a steady pulse throughout.

ST. LOUIS TICKLE

DAVE VAN RONK

Original release: *Live at Sir George Williams University* (1997)

An important and influential figure in the
acoustic folk revival of the sixties, Dave
Van Ronk was regarded as a benevolent
patriarch of Greenwich Village, presiding
over the coffeehouse folk culture and inspiring,
aiding and promoting various up and coming artists such as Bob Dylan, Joni Mitchell
and Tom Paxton. Nicknamed 'The Mayor of McDougal Street', Van Ronk was admired for his
physical presence and charisma while his ragtime transcriptions of standards such as
'St. Louis Tickle' have gone on to become highlights on the American Folk canon.

TURNPIKE TERROR

PETER LANG

Original release: *The Thing At
The Nursery Room Window* (1971)

A pioneer of American Primitive guitar,
Peter Lang took inspiration from the blues
of the twenties and thirties. Alongside Fahey,
Kottke and Basho, Lang helped to define acoustic music's
developing place within the vibrant and eclectic musical era of
the seventies. This version dates from Lang's appearance at Charlotte's Web
in Illinois, in 2007.

Guitar Tablature Explained

Guitar music can be notated in three different ways: on a musical stave, in tablature, and in rhythm slashes

RHYTHM SLASHES: are written above the stave. Strum chords in the rhythm indicated. Round noteheads indicate single notes.

THE MUSICAL STAVE: shows pitches and rhythms and is divided by lines into bars. Pitches are named after the first seven letters of the alphabet.

TABLATURE: graphically represents the guitar fingerboard. Each horizontal line represents a string, and each number represents a fret.

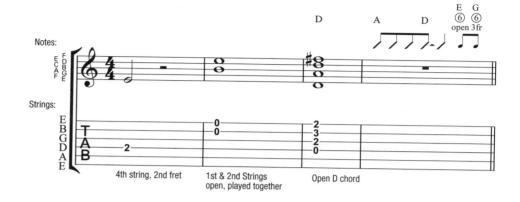

4th string, 2nd fret   1st & 2nd Strings open, played together   Open D chord

SEMI-TONE BEND: Strike the note and bend up a semi-tone (½ step).

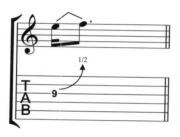

WHOLE-TONE BEND: Strike the note and bend up a whole-tone (full step).

GRACE NOTE BEND: Strike the note and bend as indicated. Play the first note as quickly as possible.

QUARTER-TONE BEND: Strike the note and bend up a ¼ step

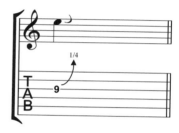

BEND & RELEASE: Strike the note and bend up as indicated, then release back to the original note.

COMPOUND BEND & RELEASE: Strike the note and bend and down in the rhythm indicated.

PRE-BEND: Bend the note as indicated, then strike it.

PRE-BEND & RELEASE: Bend the note as indicated. Strike it and release the note back to the original pitch.

HAMMER-ON: Strike the first note with one finger, then sound the second note (on the same string) with another finger by fretting it without picking.

PULL-OFF: Place both fingers on the note to be sounded, strike the first note and without picking, pull the finger off to sound the second note.

LEGATO SLIDE (GLISS): Strike the first note and then slide the same fret-hand finger up or down to the second note. The second note is not struck.

MUFFLED STRINGS: A percussive sound is produced by laying the first hand across the string(s) without depressing, and striking them with the pick hand.

NATURAL HARMONIC: Strike the note while the fret-hand lightly touches the string directly over the fret indicated.

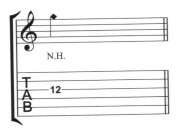

ARTIFICIAL HARMONIC: Fret lower note; with first finger of picking hand lightly touch string an octave above (fret position shown in parentheses) while striking string.

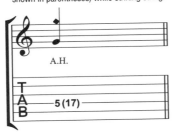

PERCUSSIVE NOTES: Strike body of guitar; the sound will vary depending on the area struck.

TREMOLO GLISSANDO: Strike the note rapidly then move the fretting hand down the neck.

TAP HARMONIC: The note is fretted normally and a harmonic is produced by 'slapping' or tapping the fret indicated in brackets (which will be twelve frets higher than the fretted note.)

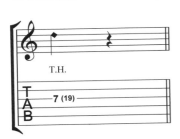

TAPPING: Hammer ('tap') the fret indicated with the pick-hand index or middle finger and pull-off to the note fretted by the fret hand.

PINCH HARMONIC: The note is fretted normally and a harmonic is produced by adding the edge of the thumb or the tip of the index finger of the pick hand to the normal pick attack.

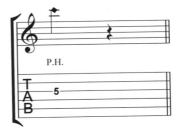

ARTIFICIAL HARMONIC: The note is fretted normally and a harmonic is produced by gently resting the pick hand's index finger directly above the indicated fret (in brackets) while plucking the appropriate string.

TRILL: Very rapidly alternate between the notes indicated by continuously hammering-on and pulling-off.

RAKE: Drag the pick across the strings with a single motion.

TREMOLO PICKING: The note is picked as rapidly and continously as possible.

ARPEGGIATE: Play the notes of the chord indicated by quickly rolling them from bottom to top.

ADDITIONAL MUSICAL DEFINITIONS

 (accent) — Accentuate note (play it louder).

D.S. al Coda — Go back to the sign (𝄋), then play until the bar marked *To Coda* ⊕ then skip to the section marked ⊕ *Coda* .

 (accent) — Accentuate note with greater intensity.

D.C. al Fine — Go back to the beginning of the song and play until the bar marked *Fine*.

 (staccato) — Shorten time value of note.

tacet — Instrument is silent (drops out).

⊓ — Downstroke

∨ — Upstroke

 — Repeat bars between signs.

NOTE: Tablature numbers in brackets mean:
1. The note is sustained, but a new articulation (such as hammer on or slide) begins
2. A note may be fretted but not necessarily played.

When a repeat section has different endings, play the first ending only the first time and the second ending only the second time.

EMBRYONIC JOURNEY

Music by Jorma Kaukonen

*Chord names represent implied harmony

FREIGHT TRAIN

Words & Music by Elizabeth Cotten, Paul James & Frederick Williams

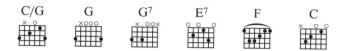

To match recording, tune guitar down one whole tone.

♩ = 100

Acoustic steel string guitar

Freight train, freight train run so fast,
freight train, freight train run so fast.
Please don't tell what train I'm on, they won't

17

Verse 2:
When I'm dead and in my grave,
No more good times will I crave.
Place the stones at my head and feet,
Tell 'em all that I've gone to sleep.

Verse 3:
When I die, Lord bury me deep,
Way down on old Chestnut Street.
So I can hear old number nine
As she comes rolling by.

Verse 4:
When I die, Lord bury me deep,
Way down on old Chestnut Street.
Place the stones at my head and feet,
Tell 'em all that I've gone to sleep.

GIRL FROM THE NORTH COUNTRY

Words & Music by Bob Dylan

Capo 3rd fret

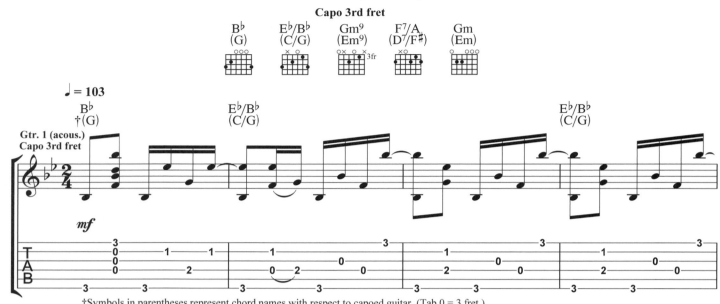

†Symbols in parentheses represent chord names with respect to capoed guitar. (Tab 0 = 3 fret.)
Symbols above represent actual sounding chords.

1. Well, if _____ you're
2. Well, if you go _____
5. So if _____ you're

tra - vel - in' ____ in the north _____ coun - try fair, _____
____ when ____ the snow - flakes storm, _____
tra - vel - in' ____ in the north _____ coun - try fair, _____

21

1.

2.

3. Please see for me if her hair _____ hangs long,

(4.) wond - er - in' if she re - mem - bers me at all, _____

if it rolls _____ and flows all ____ down her breast, _

ma - ny times I've of - ten prayed _

A HAZY SHADE OF WINTER

Words & Music by Paul Simon

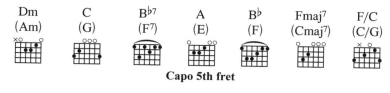

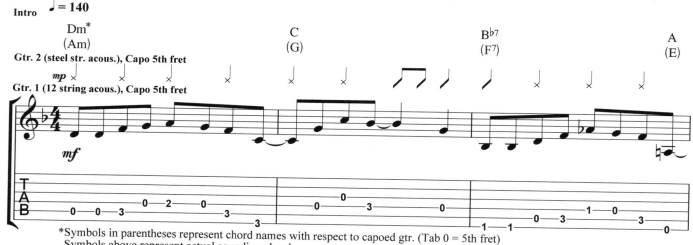

*Symbols in parentheses represent chord names with respect to capoed gtr. (Tab 0 = 5th fret)
Symbols above represent actual sounding chords

for my__ pos - si - bi - li - ties_____

I was so

hard__ to please.

But look a - round____

the leaves are brown__

and the sky____

is a ha - zy shade__ of win -

2. Hear the Sal - va - tion Ar - my_ band

3. Hang on to your hopes my_ friend,

- ter.

28

CANDY MAN BLUES

Words & Music by John Hurt

To match recording, tune guitar up a semitone or capo at 1st fret

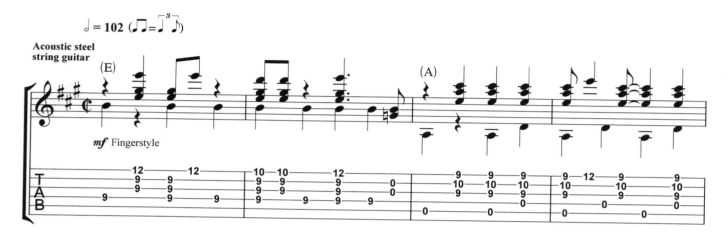

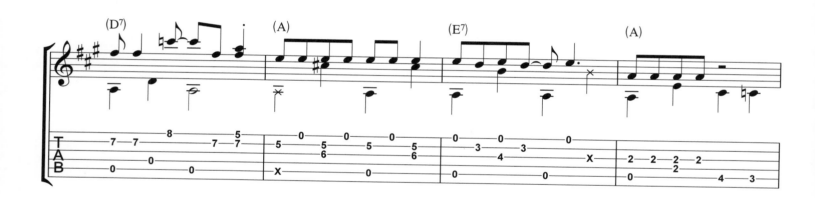

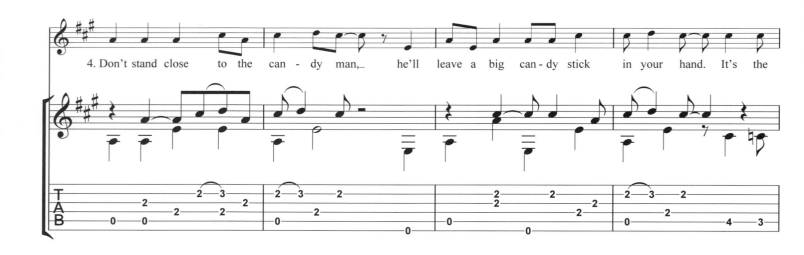

4. Don't stand close to the can-dy man,__ he'll leave a big can-dy stick in your hand. It's the

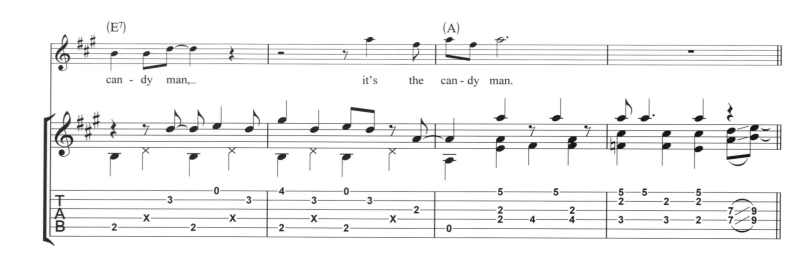

can-dy man,__ it's the can-dy man.

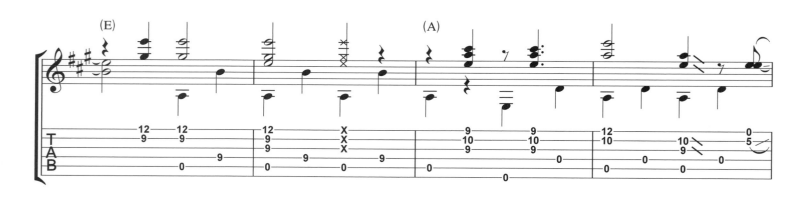

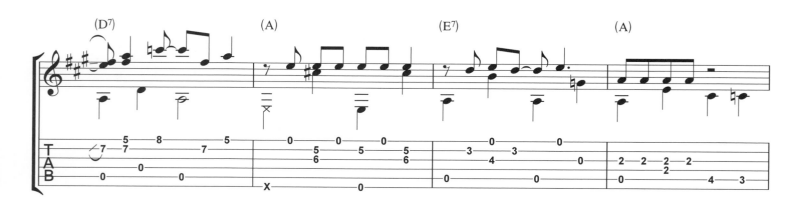

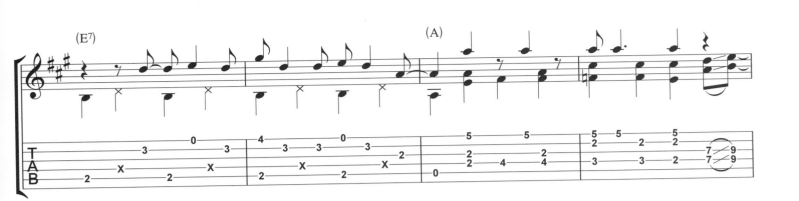

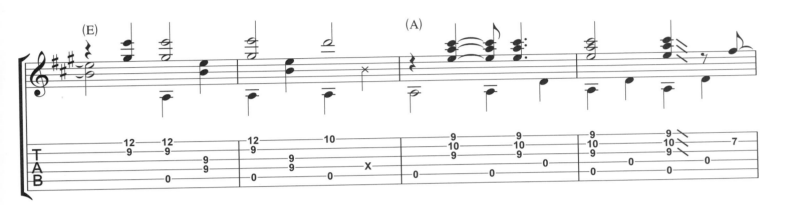

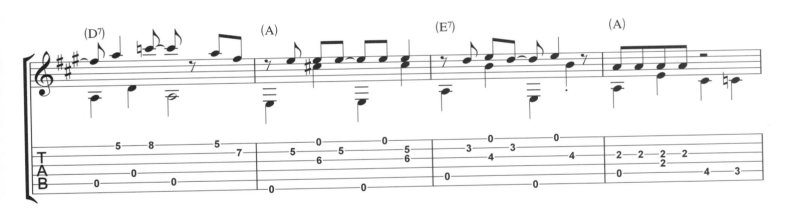

D.S. al Coda

5. He

35

⊕ *Coda*

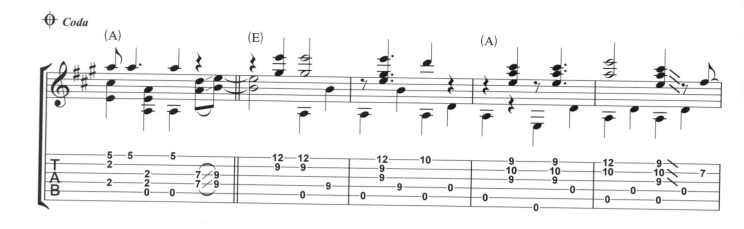

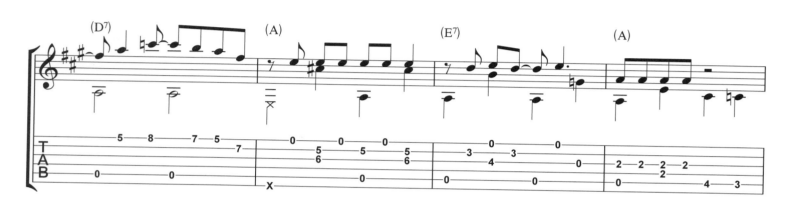

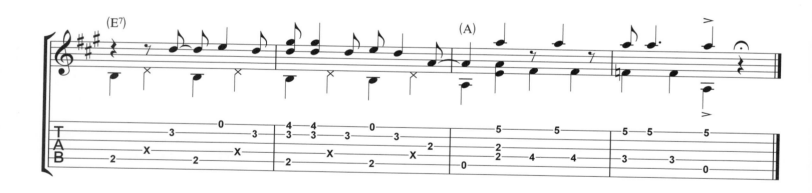

Verse 5:
He sold some candy to sister Bad,
The very next day she took all he had.
It's the candy man,
It's the candy man.

Verse 6:
If you try his candy, good friend of mine,
You sure will want it for a long long time.
It's the candy man,
Sweet candy man.

Verse 7:
His stick candy don't melt away,
It just gets better, so the ladies say.
It's the candy man,
It's the candy man.

'Ian and Nisa' was recorded in 1979 and issued in 1980 on the Takoma LP *Michael Gulezian/Unspoken Intentions*. This transcription corresponds to the recording with the exception of a few minor revisions which bring it in line with Michael's current thinking and best performance practice.

When Michael originally recorded 'Ian and Nisa' in 1979, he used metal finger-picks on *i*, *m* and *a*, and a plastic thumbpick. But by 1983 he had already stopped using picks and, in fact, began discouraging their use. This transcription is based on his original technical approach, and it can be played with picks or without. Michael executes many of the descending slurs that occur in this piece by pushing upward and outward instead of the more conventional pulling downward and outward. This produces a slightly softer articulation and, in many cases, is used to avoid touching the lower adjacent string.

note 1
In these instances, Michael is sliding while finessing a left-hand finger shift.

note 2
On the second beat, Michael's right-hand thumb and middle finger come to rest on the third and first strings respectively. Audible percussion is produced by the right hand coming down on the strings and also by the right-hand little finger coming down on the top of the guitar just below the first string.

note 3
Here Michael uses an exaggerated outward plucking motion, generated from the elbow, in which the right hand quickly pulls away from the strings. This produces an accented note with a distinctive tone colour.

RIGHT-HAND FINGERING:
These are the first letters of the Spanish words for the digits:

pulgar - thumb
indice - index finger
medio - middle finger
anlar - ring finger
These symbols are only used for right-hand fingerings.

p i m a

SLUR (HAMMER-ON, PULL-OFF):
A curved line between two different numbers indicates a slur. If the second number is higher, the second note is executed by pulling off. (A hammer-on or pull-off can be executed by the right or left hand. Look for right- or left- hand editing.)

LEFT-HAND FINGERING:
① – first (index) finger
② – second (middle) finger
③ – third (ring) finger
④ – fourth (little) finger
The circle helps distinguish these left-hand fingerings from other symbols in the tablature. These symbols are used only for left-hand fingerings.

HAMMER-ON FROM NOWHERE:
A short slur before a number indicates that the note is hammered on from nowhere. In other words, the string has not been plucked immediately prior to hammering on. (A hammer-on from nowhere can be executed by the right or left hand. Look for right- or left-hand editing.) A short slur is also used at the beginning of a system to show the continuation of a tie or slur.

GUIDE FINGER:
A dash before a left-hand finger number indicates that that left-hand finger has been used on that string immediately prior and has guided along that string to reach the current fret.

-①
-②

VIBRATO:
There are three elements to the notation of vibrato. The letter represents the kind of vibrato (vertical, horizontal or neck). The length of the wavy line represents the duration of the vibrato. The speed of the vibrato is shown either fast or slow.

BARRE:
This symbol is used to show the number of strings held by and the position of a barre. A line with a downward termination shows the duration of the barre. If no fraction is used, all six strings are enclosed. If used with a fraction, the number of strings indicated is presumed to begin with the first string. If used in conjunction with a bracket, only strings included in the bracket are barred.

SNARE:
This effect is produced by the right coming down on the strings. The percussion can be caused either by the strings hitting the frets or just by the backs of the nails hitting the strings.

PARENTHESES:
Parentheses enclose a note that is fingered but not played.

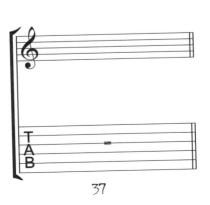

IAN AND NISA

Music by Michael Gulezian

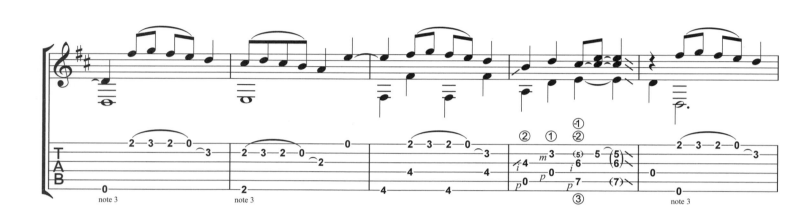

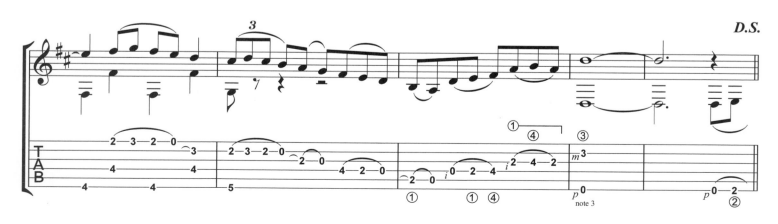

41

ICE MINER

Music by Leo Kottke

†Symbols in parentheses represent chord names with respect to capoed guitar. Symbols above represent actual sounding chords. (TAB 0=2nd fret.)

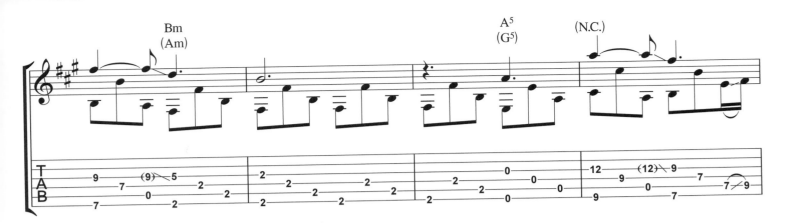

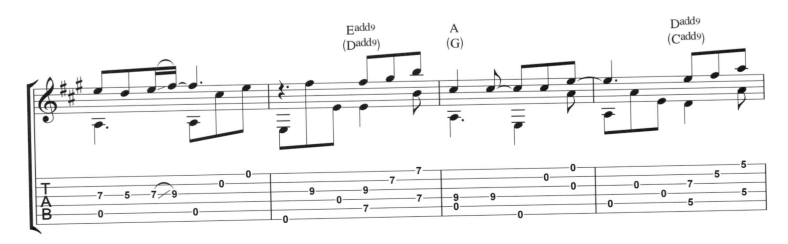

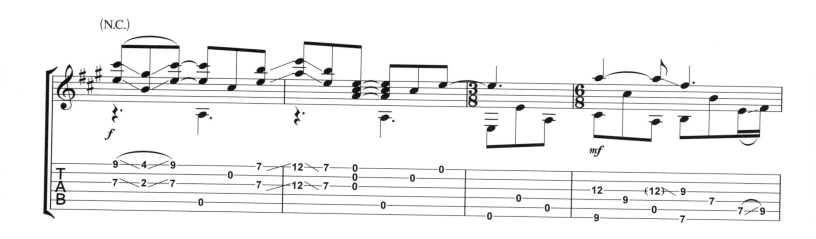

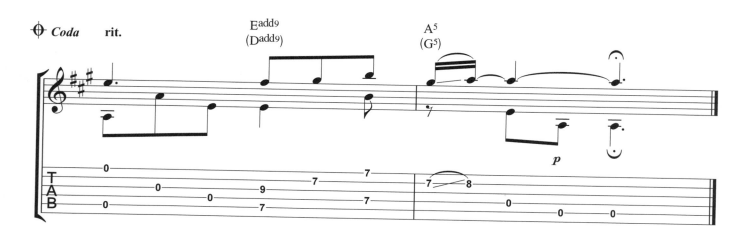

44

ST. LOUIS TICKLE

Music by Glen Snelgrove

*Chord names represent implied harmony

ON THE SUNNY
SIDE OF THE OCEAN

Music by John Fahey

Tuning
6 = D 3 = G
5 = G 2 = B
4 = D 1 = D

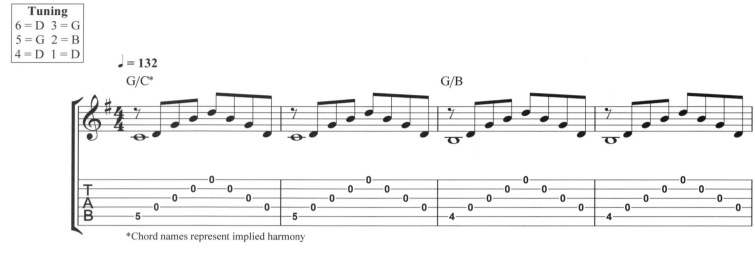

*Chord names represent implied harmony

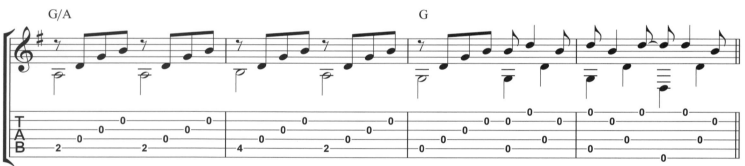

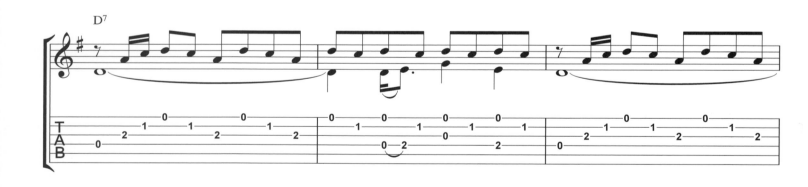

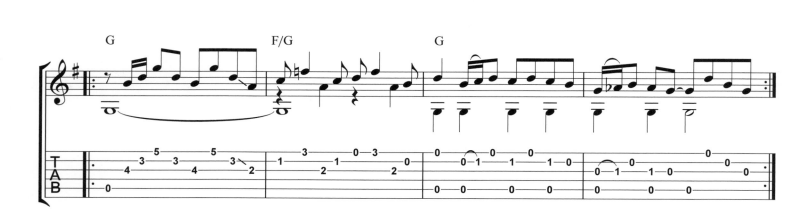

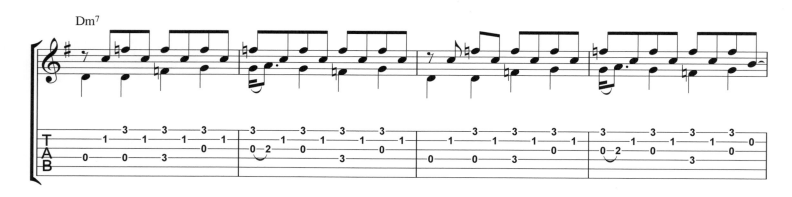

THE POOR PEOPLE OF PARIS

Words by Rene Rouzaud
Music by Margeurite Monnot

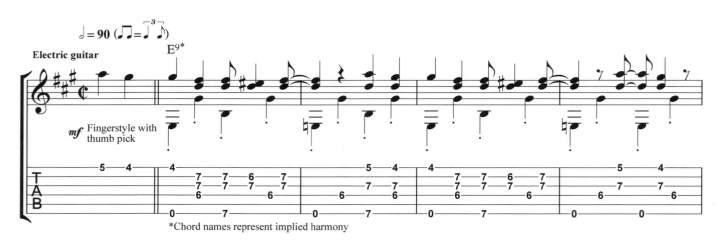

*Chord names represent implied harmony

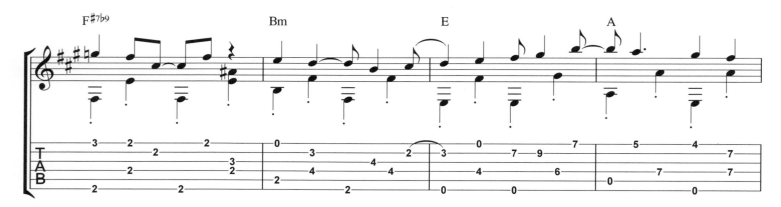

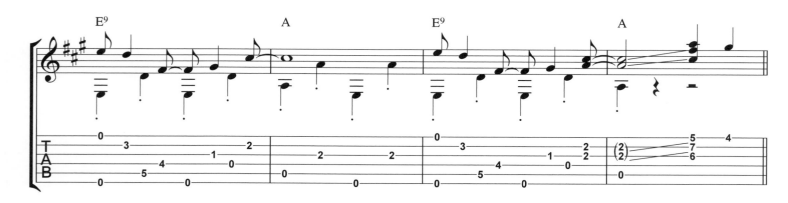

57

REDWOOD RAMBLE

Music by Robbie Basho

TURNPIKE TERROR

Music by Peter Lang

Tuning
6 = C 3 = E
5 = G 2 = G
4 = C 1 = C

*Chord names represent implied harmony